This

book belongs to:

centum

Published 2013. Centum Books Ltd.
Unit 1, Upside Station Building Solsbro Road,
Torquay, Devon, UK, TQ26FD

Contents

Welcome

Welcome to Tickety Toc's fun-packed annual! It's full of games, activities and stories for you to enjoy with your Chime Time friends.

Tommy and Tallulah can't wait for you to join them on their Tickety adventures. But they need your help, too. Everyone in Tickety Town has lost something special in the pages of the annual.

Keep a lookout, and write down the page number where you find each one.

Tommy's drum is on page:

Tallulah's bell is on page:

Madame Au Lait's Ping-Pong bat is on page:

McCoggins's spanner is on page:

Pufferty's ball is on page:

Hello Tommy!

Tommy loves adventures!

Together with his twin sister Tallulah, he is always on the lookout for fun and excitement.

Tommy enjoys fixing things and working out how to solve problems.

Whenever he's with Tallulah, he feels as if can do anything!

Tommy plays the drum at Chime Time and loves playing football.

What's your favourite thing about Tommy?

Hello Tallulah!

Tallulah has a wonderful imagination.

She is brimming with ideas, and she loves sharing them with her twin brother Tommy.

Tallulah gets so excited and is full of creativity and imagination.

Tallulah loves playing her trumpet and always comes up with a plan to solve problems.

What do you like best about Tallulah?

Hello Pufferty!

Pufferty loves his job!

He helps everyone in Tickety Town to get around. All you have to do is call his name, and he'll be right by your side.

Pufferty's favourite time of the day is Chime Time when he delivers Tommy and Tallulah on time.

What would you say to Pufferty if you met him?

Pufferty loves chasing his ball along the tracks!

Hello McCoggins!

McCoggins has a workshop which is full of useful spanners and screwdrivers!

There is nothing that McCoggins can't mend.

He fixes everything in Tickety Town that needs fixing.

McCoggins is very kind and he loves inventing. He has made lots of amazing things!

What would you like McCoggins to invent for you?

Hello Hopparoo!

Hopparoo is a bouncing bunny who loves carrots.

He jumps up extra-high whenever he gets excited, and causes all sorts of mischief along the way!

Hopparoo is the bouncing bunny with the non-stop hop!

How high can you jump?

Hello Chikidee!

Chikidee also loves knitting and playing Ping-Pong!

Chikidee sits high above the Clockhouse, keeping an eye on the weather.

She loves giving out weather reports to all her Tickety Town friends!

What is the weather like outside your window?

Hello Madame Au Lait!

Everyone in Tickety Town loves Madame Au Lait.

She has a big heart and an even bigger appetite.

Most of all she enjoys cooking, and her friends enjoy eating the yummy things she makes!

Madame Au Lait is a Taekwondo expert and just loves cooking!

What's your favourite meal?

Hello Battersby!

Battersby runs an amazing shop that stocks everything his customers might ever need.

He is very helpful, but he is always falling asleep at the wrong moment!

Battersby sells bells, balls, bugles, biscuits and bananas!

What would you buy from Battersby's shop?

Hello Lopsiloo!

Tickety Town's fruit and vegetables are delivered by Lopsiloo!

Lopsiloo is very proud of the food she grows, and she spends all her spare time in her garden growing vegetables.

Lopsiloo is a super-fast snail and she calls vegetables 'vegetabubbles.'

What's your favourite vegetable?

Hello Tooteroo!

Tooteroo is a little owl who enjoys watching the world around him.

He is very interested in anything new, but he's also a bit unlucky!

Tooteroo doesn't speak at all, but he does have lots of funny actions!

What's your favourite joke?

Hello Spring Chicks!

Spring Chicks are very greedy and their favourite food is 'tomoootoes.'

Mother Hen finds it hard to keep her three babies under control.

The Spring Chicks like to wander around looking for food. It's lucky they're so cute!

What is your favourite season?

Double Trouble

Tommy and Tallulah love this picture of their friends. But there are five differences between the two photos. Can you spot them all?

See answers on page 93.

What's the Time?

The Spring Chicks are learning to tell the time. Can you help them?

Draw lines to match each time with the correct clock.

1.

5.

2.

a. Four o'clock
b. One o'clock
c. Six o'clock
d. Ten o'clock
e. Nine o'clock

4.

3.

See answers on page 93.

Trainspotting

Tommy

Tallulah

Hopparoo

chikidee

Battersby

16

Toot toot! Pufferty is taking his friends for a ride. Who's on board today? Look carefully at the picture and tick each face you spot.

See answers on page 93.

McCoggins

Lopsiloo

Tooteroo

Spring Chicks

Madame Au Lait

What's the Time, Tallulah?
It's Bake a Cake Time!

Yes! Tommy and Tallulah are very excited.
They are going to bake a cake with Madame Au Lait.
"Let's bake a Sticky Icky carroty cake!" says Madame Au Lait.
Tommy and Tallulah can't wait to start.

At that moment,
Chikidee arrives.
"Ready for Ping–Pong,
Madame Au Lait?"
she asks.

Oh no! Madame Au Lait
had forgotten about
Ping–Pong! What is she
going to do?

Tommy and Tallulah have an idea. "We could bake the carroty cake, Madame Au Lait."

Madame Au Lait isn't sure, but Tommy and Tallulah shoo her towards the door. "Okay, my little Chime Timers," she says. "But make sure you stick to the recipe. Mooo!"

"LET'S BAKE THAT CAKE!" shout Tommy and Tallulah.

The recipe says that they need one small bag of carroty cake mix.

Tommy picks up the bag, but on his way back he trips over a ball.

Oops! The bag flies out of his hands and disappears through the window!

"Sorry, Tallulah," says Tommy.

"Don't worry, Tommy!" says Tallulah. "Let's get some more from Battersby's store. I want to bake THE BEST CAKE EVER!

Tommy and Tallulah whistle for Pufferty. He comes straight away.
"Here I am! Can we go now? Anywhere you want!"

"To Battersby's shop, please!" says Tallulah.

Pufferty races through Tickety Town. McCoggins is in the town square.

"We're going to bake a cake!" shouts Tommy.

"Would you like some?" asks Tallulah.

"OF COURSE I'D LIKE SOME!" says McCoggins.

Battersby is asleep in his shop. Tommy and Tallulah ring the bell and wake him up. PING! "It's Bake A Cake time!" says Tommy.

Hopparoo is close by. He bounces with joy when he hears about the cake!

"One small bag of carroty cake mix, please, Battersby," says Tallulah.

"SMALL?" says Hopparoo, sounding disappointed.

Tommy and Tallulah whisper to each other.

"Make that one super duper enormously gigantic bag of carroty cake mix please, Battersby!" says Tallulah.

"How about three of them!" says Tommy.

Tallulah twirls with excitement!

"Yes!" she says. "If our cake's going to be the best cake ever, it's got to be bigger!"

Pufferty takes Tommy and Tallulah back to Tic Toc house.
Madame Au Lait is still playing Ping-Pong.

"We're going to bake the best cake you've ever seen!" Tallulah calls.

"I'll pop it in the oven as soon as you're ready," says Madame Au Lait.

Tommy and Tallulah
pour the cake mix
into a bowl.
Easypeasy!
Lemon squeezy!

"We're going to
need a bigger bowl,"
says Tallulah.

Tommy and Tallulah
find a GIANT bowl.

"That's more like it!"
says Tommy.

Tommy empties a sack of cake mix into the bowl.

"This is going to be the best carroty cake ever!" Tallulah says.

Tommy and Tallulah have forgotten all about following the recipe.
They're too busy having fun!

Madame Au Lait has won her Ping-Pong match.

"The cake's ready to bake!" call Tommy and Tallulah.

"There it is, Madame Au Lait," says Tommy. "Ready to bake!"

Madame Au Lait pushes the cake tin into the oven.
"In we go! Moo!" She says. "That'll be ready to eat after Chime Time."

"Now, let's tidy this kitchen!"

Tommy washes the dishes and Tallulah dries them with a tea towel. Madame Au Lait sweeps the floor.

No one notices that the cake is oozing out of the oven!
"Mmm, our cake smells lovely," says Tallulah.

Madame Au Lait turns around and gasps. The oven is bulging with cake!
"You did both follow my recipe didn't you?" asks Madame Au Lait.

Tommy and Tallulah gulp.
"For a bit . . ." says Tommy.

"Abandon kitchen!" Madame Au Lait cries. "That cake is out of control!"

KABLAMMMMM!
The cake explodes all over Tickety Town!

Tommy and Tallulah didn't mean to cause so much trouble.

"We're sorry, Madame Au Lait," says Tommy.

"We just wanted to bake the best cake ever," says Tallulah.

"Moo-hoo-hooho!" chuckles Madame Au Lait. "Well you certainly baked the messiest. What a stickety mess!"

Then McCoggins arrives with some terrible news.
"Pufferty can't move! He's completely stuck in carroty cake!"

We can't do Chime Time without him!" cry Tommy and Tallulah.

Pufferty is well and truly stuck. Everyone tries to help.
"HEAVE!" They push as hard as they can, but Pufferty just won't budge.

"We'll never get him to Chime Time!" says Tallulah.

Suddenly Madame Au Lait has an idea. Perhaps Pufferty's squeaky ball can help!

Tommy and Tallulah throw the squeaky ball.
"FETCH, Pufferty!" says Tommy.

Pufferty heaves himself free.
"Mine! Woof woof!"

"Quick Pufferty – to the clock!" says Tommy.

Pufferty races towards the Clockhouse.

Tommy and Tallulah clean themselves up.

Hurray! Tommy and Tallulah are just in time for Chime Time!

Late Delivery

Help Lopsiloo deliver her vegetables to Battersby's shop on time by taking a shortcut through the maze.

Start

Lopsiloo

is running late and the clock is ticking!

End

See answers on page 93.

Where's the Word?
Tick Tock Tastic!

Easy Peasy Lemon Squeezy!

Five of Tommy and Tallulah's favourite words are hidden inside this grid. Ask a grown-up to help you find them all.

CLOCK

CAKE

FUN

CHIME

TIME

C	L	O	C	K	W	E	R
T	Y	U	A	I	O	P	A
S	D	F	K	G	H	J	K
K	L	Z	E	X	C	V	C
B	N	N	M	Q	W	W	H
W	A	V	F	U	N	B	I
B	R	Q	D	B	A	N	M
I	K	G	S	T	I	M	E

See answers on page 93.

29

Hungry Friends

Someone has been munching Lopsiloo's vegetables! Follow the lines to find out who has been nibbling these tasty treats.

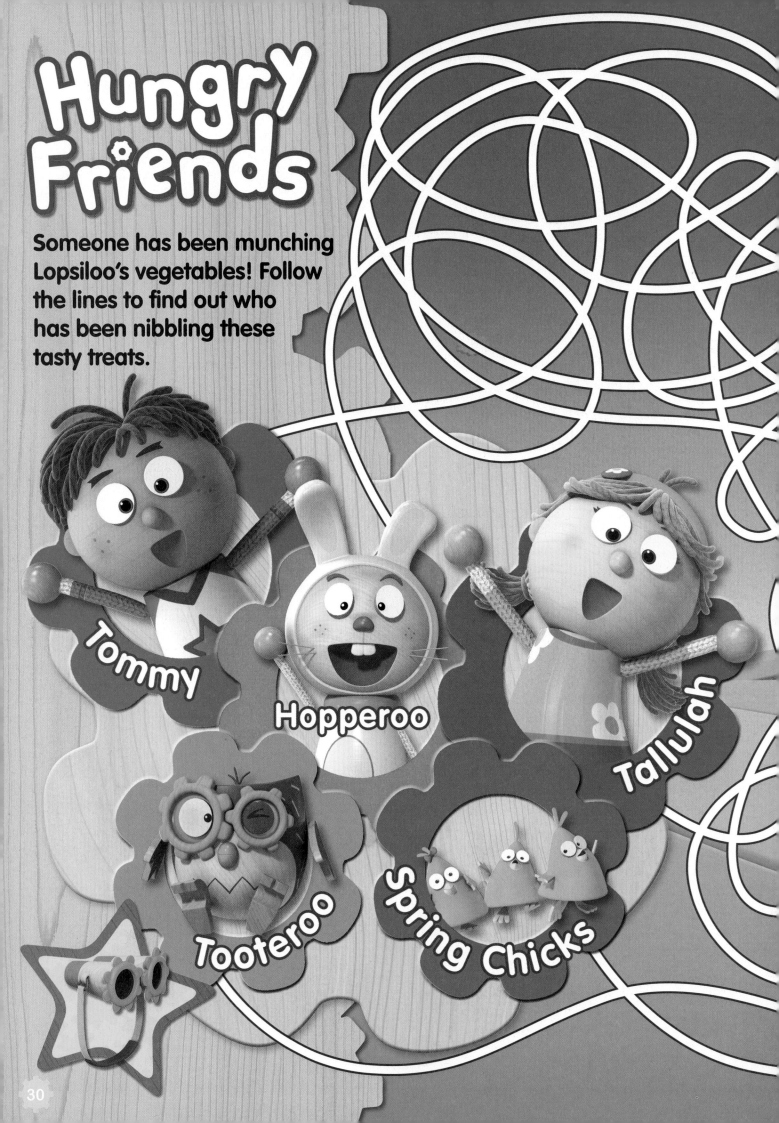

Tommy

Hopperoo

Tallulah

Tooteroo

Spring Chicks

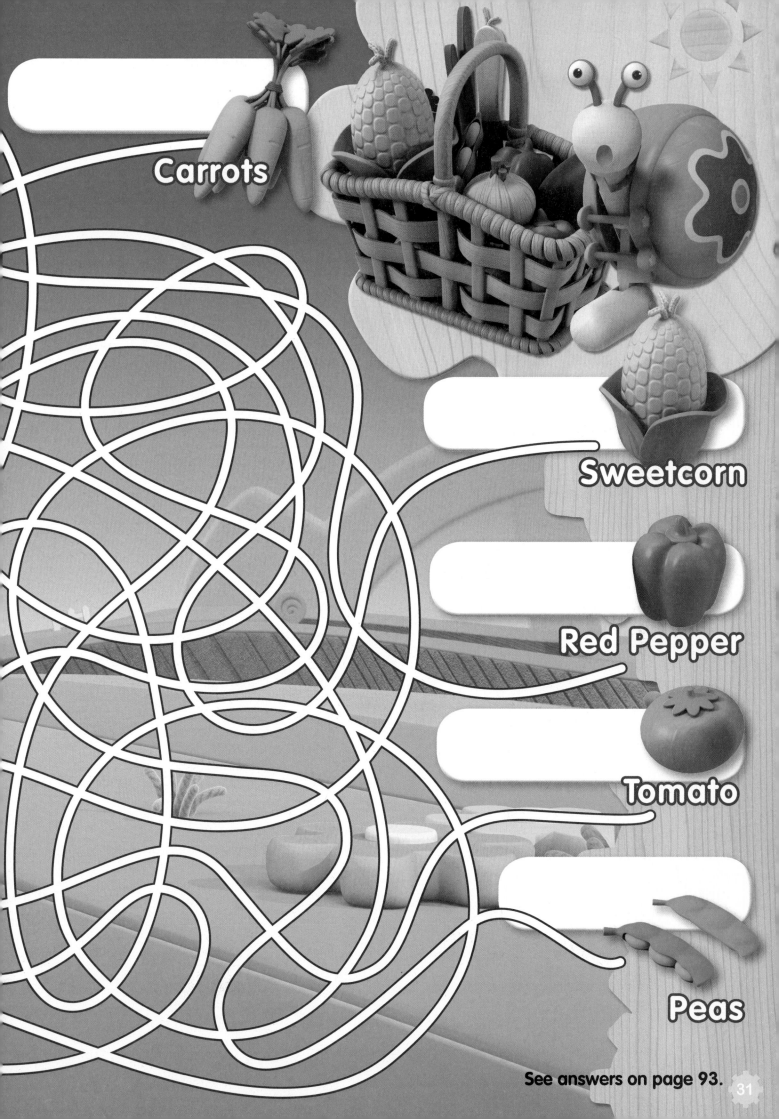

Carrots

Sweetcorn

Red Pepper

Tomato

Peas

See answers on page 93.

Dot to Dot

Who is chatting to Chikidee?

Join the dots to find out.

Tickety Twins!

Tommy & Tallulah

33

Madame Au Lait's Banana Cake

Do you like baking? Moo-ly wooly!

Follow Madame Au Lait's instructions and make a yummy cake to share with your friends.

Ask a grown-up to help you use the oven.

Mooooooooo!

34

Equipment

Loaf tin
Greaseproof paper
Wooden spoon
Fork or potato masher
Sieve
A grown-up
to help you

Ingredients

4oz butter
6oz sugar
2 eggs
2 large bananas
1 tbsp milk
1 tsp vanilla essence
8oz self-raising flour
½ tsp ground cinnamon

Method

1. Ask your grown-up to preheat the oven to 180°C.
2. Grease a loaf tin and line it with greaseproof paper.
3. Use a fork or a potato masher to mash the bananas until they are smooth.
4. Cream the butter and sugar together with a wooden spoon, until it is pale and fluffy.
5. Beat the eggs and mix them with the butter and sugar.
6. Mix in the mashed bananas, milk and vanilla essence.
7. Sieve the flour and cinnamon into the mixture and stir well.
8. Pour the mixture into the loaf tin.
9. Ask your grown-up to bake the cake for 40-60 minutes.
10. When the cake is cooked, ask your grown-up to take it out of the oven and cool it on a wire rack.

Finally! Enjoy your banana cake with friends.

Weather Time

Breakfast time

You can help Chickidee to forecast the weather! Look at the pictures and write down what you think the weather will be like today.

Dinner time

Tea time

Bed time

See answers on page 93.

Doodle Designer

Use your crayons to finish McCoggins's new invention.

What a Tickety Pickle!

What do you think it does?

Give it an exciting name!

Hide and Seek

The residents of Tickety Town are playing hide and seek!

See answers on page 93.

Can you help Tommy to find everyone and everything on his list?

Tick each one you find.

	Tommy	✓
Tallulah		
	Lopsiloo	
Hopparoo		
	Chikidee	
Tooteroo		
	Spring Chicks	
Trumpet		
	Hammock	
Bell		
	Drum	
Net		
	Basket	
Football		
	Watering can	
Toolbox		

Happy Gardener

Lopsiloo works hard in her vegetable garden.

Colour in this busy snail and her crop.

Lopsiloo

40

Ball Sale

Sleepy Battersby has lots of balls for sale in his shop.

How many balls can you count?

See answer on page 93.

41

It's Time to Chime!

It's almost Chime Time, but Pufferty has overslept! Can you help Tommy and Tallulah reach the clock and do their special job?

You will need

2 dice
A marker for each player
Timer

Rules

1. Set the timer for fifteen minutes.
2. Roll the dice and move along the board.
3. If you land on an action circle, do what it says.
4. The winner is the player who reaches the clock before the timer goes off!

Start

1

2

3

7

9

Lopsiloo gives you a shiny red apple. Go forward two spaces.

You stop to say good morning to Chikidee. Go back one space.

Finish

20

19

18

You find a shortcut through Tickety Town. Have another turn.

12

You borrow McCoggins's scooter. Go forward one space.

10

13

16

14

Madame Au Lait asks you to help her bake a cake. Go back three spaces.

Tickety Town

43

Gardening with Lopsiloo

Equipment

A packet of cress seeds

Clean, empty yoghurt pot

Kitchen roll

Cotton wool

Tickety Town's delivery snail loves working in her garden. Now you can be just like Lopsiloo and grow your own food. Follow these simple steps to grow your own cress.

1. Fold up some kitchen roll so that it will fit into the yoghurt pot. Then wet it and put it in the bottom of the pot.

2. Put some wet cotton wool on top of the kitchen roll. Leave a 2cm gap between the cotton wool and the top of the pot.

3. Scatter some cress seeds (about a teaspoon full) onto the cotton wool. Spread them out evenly and press them down gently.

4. Put the yoghurt pot in a warm, sunny place like a windowsill.

5. Wait a few days for the cress to grow.

6. Snip off the yummy cress and eat it in your sandwiches!

45

What's the Time, Tallulah?
It's Dress-Up Time!

"Let's look in the dress-up box!" says Tommy.

The dress-up box is full of exciting costumes. Tallulah rummages in the box. "I'm not wearing a pink tutu!" says Tommy.

"Ho Yes!" says Tommy. "Look at these."

Two silly masks! "I like those!" says Tallulah.

Tommy and Tallulah have fun scaring each other.

"Dress-Up Time is the best time ever!" says Tallulah.

46

Madame Au Lait is watering her tomatoes. "Oh how moooovelous!" she says. "My tomooootoes are ripe!"

Madame Au Lait must pick her tomatoes before the Spring Chicks gobble them up. "Where there's a tomooooto, there's always a Spring Chick!"

Madame Au Lait goes inside to fetch a basket.

The Spring Chicks come running to the tomato plant.

Closer and closer!

ROAR! Tommy and Tallulah are wearing their masks. The Spring Chicks run away!

"It's only us," says Tommy.

He takes off his mask. The Spring Chicks are very surprised!

Tommy and Tallulah put on their masks again.
"BOO!"
The Spring Chicks giggle and run away. They love this game!

The Spring Chicks have forgotten all about the tomatoes. Madame Au Lait is very pleased.
"Let's see who else we can surprise," says Tommy.

Hopparoo is asleep in his hammock.

"Are you ready, Tommy?" asks Tallulah.
"I'm ready if you're ready," says Tommy with a giggle.

"BOO!"

Hopparoo opens one eye and yawns
"Nice masks," he says. Then his ears flop down over his eyes.

"I thought he would be surprised," says Tommy.

Suddenly Hopparoo jumps up!
"BADOOOO!" he shouts. "Now that's a surprise!"

"You wait, Hopparoo," says Tallulah. "You'll be really, really surprised!"

"Hugely, massively, super-nuper-duperly really surprised!" says Tommy.

Tommy and Tallulah dress up to surprise Hopparoo. Deely boppers and party blowers. PWEEEE! But Hopparoo just smiles and stretches.

"Time to try something else," says Tommy.

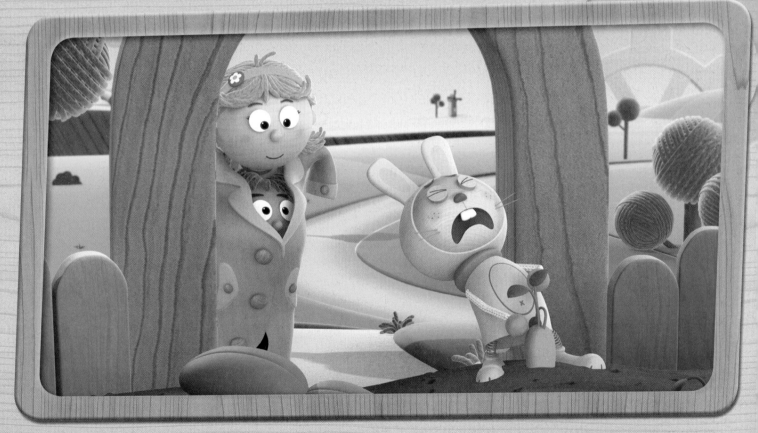

Hopparoo bounces up to Lopsiloo's garden gate. He is feeling peckish, and Lopsiloo's carrots look very tasty!

Tommy and Tallulah creep up behind him. They are wearing Madame Au Lait's coat.

Hopparoo pulls on a carrot. POP! He falls backwards and bumps into Tommy and Tallulah.

FLOP! They fall into Lopsiloo's compost heap!
Oh no! Tommy and Tallulah are covered in compost!

"I'm not sure we're that good at surprising Hopparoo, Tommy," says Tallulah.

"Well if you're not sure, I'm not sure either," Tommy says.

Lopsiloo wants to know what Hopparoo is doing with her carrot.
"The carrot just sort of jumped into my hand," he says.

Just then, Lopsiloo sees Tommy and Tallulah in the compost heap.
"EEEEK" she cries.

"Waggghhh!" yells Hopparoo. Tommy and Tallulah look really scary!

"We gave Hopparoo a super-nuper-duper surprise!" says Tallulah.

"Our dress-up disguise did the trick," says Tommy. "With a bit of mud of course!"

The Spring Chicks get a big surprise when they see Tommy and Tallulah. They're so scared that they run to hide in the Clockhouse!

Tommy and Tallulah pull off the coat.

"We've got to tell them it's us!" says Tallulah.

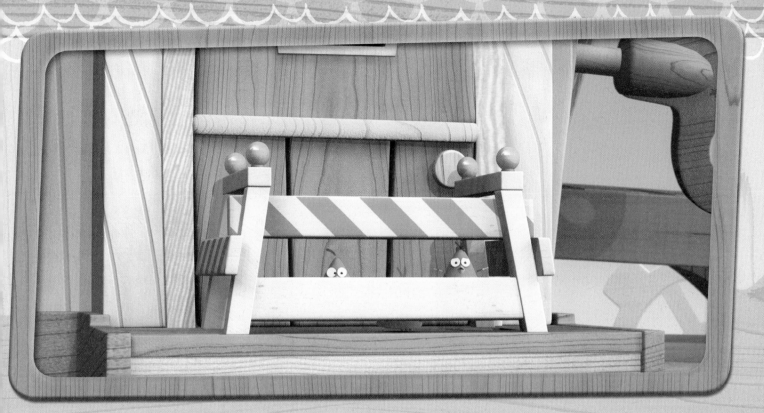

The Spring Chicks make a lot of loud noises. Clatter! Clunk! Clatter!

The Spring Chicks have built a barrier in front of the Clockhouse door!

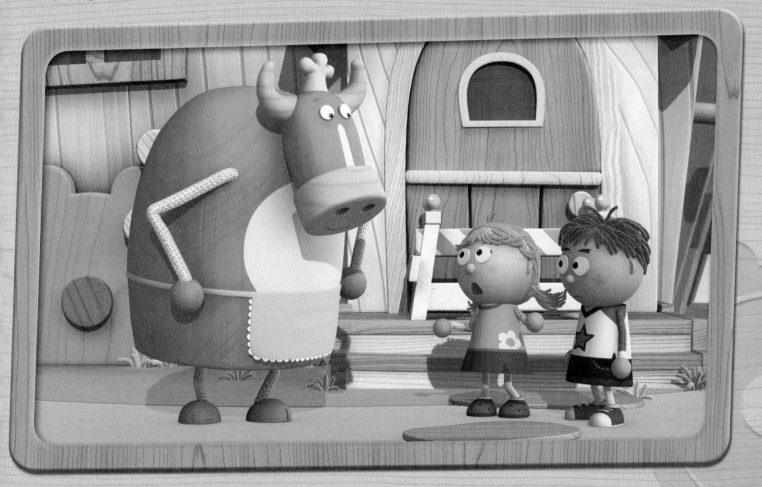

When Madame Au Lait arrives, Tommy and Tallulah explain what happened.

"We surprised them too much and now they're scared of us," says Tommy.

"And they've blocked the way to Chime Time!" Tallulah adds.

"But Chime Time is almost here!" says Madame Au Lait.

"We're going to be too late!" says Tallulah.

Everyone tries to think of a way to bring the Spring Chicks out.

"There's nothing to be afraid of," says Madame Au Lait. "I want you to come out on a count of three." But even she can't make the Spring Chicks come out.

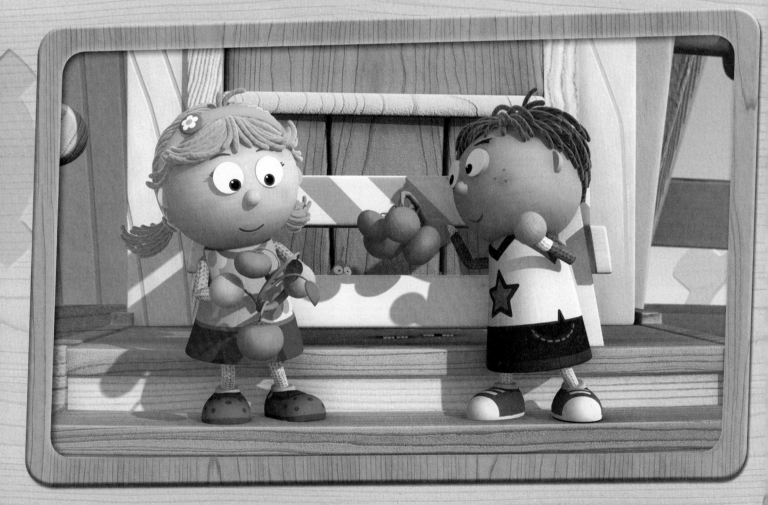

Tallulah has an idea.
"Madame Au Lait, can we have some of your tomoooootoes?" she asks.

Tommy and Tallulah take the tomatoes up to the barrier.
"Get your tomoooootoes!" shouts Tommy. "Buy one get one free! Ripe and ready! Sweet as sugar!"

Suddenly everyone hears the Spring Chicks cheeping.
The barrier is coming down!

The Spring Chicks rush to gobble up the tomatoes.
The way to the Clockhouse is clear!

Tommy and Tallulah race inside. But the sand is almost through the hourglass.

Will they be in time?

Phew! Tommy and Tallulah chime in the time – with only a second to spare.

Well done, Tommy and Tallulah!

Dress-Up Drawing

Tommy, Tallulah and Madame Au Lait love dressing up!

Draw and colour a fancy-dress costume for each of them.

56

Colouring In

Poor Chikidee has lost all her colour! Use your crayons to make her look glamorous again.

Mix and Match

Tallulah is teaching the Spring Chicks all about opposites.

Can you help? Draw lines to match the opposites.

Hot

Small

Cold

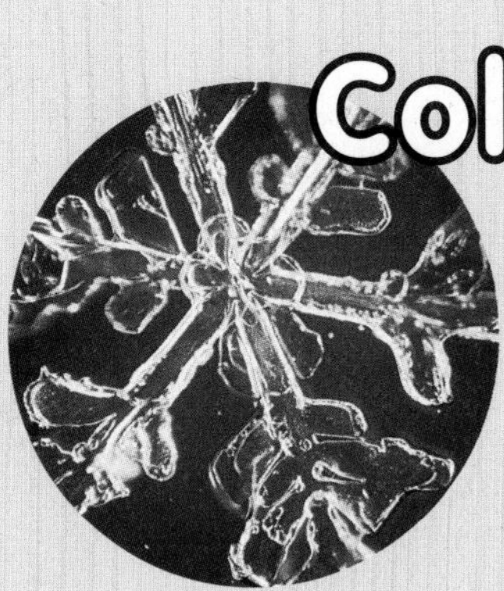

Down

Empty

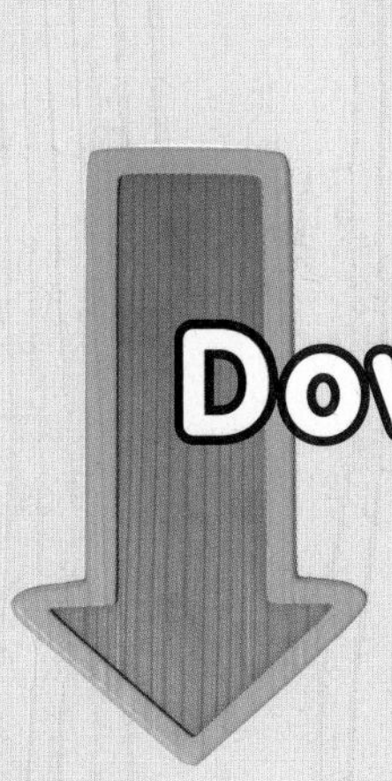

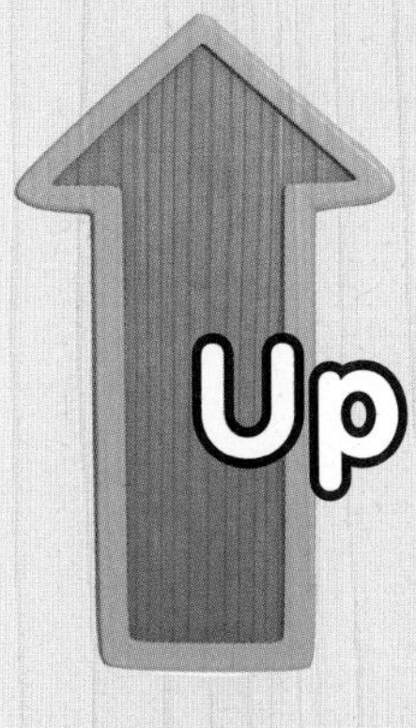

Up

Big

Full

See answers on page 93.

Writing Time

Do you know how to write these Tickety words? Use your pencil to copy over the dots. Madame Au Lait will show you the way!

Time   Time

Fun   Fun

Clock   Clock

Chime   Chime

Shop   Shop

Friends   Friends

Play   Play

Game   Game

61

Shadow Match

Can you recognise each of these shadows, Chime Timers? Draw lines to match the shadows to their owners.

1.

2.

3.

4.

5.

a.

b.

c.

d.

e.

See answers on page 93.

62

Camera Calamity

Tommy has taken some photos of his friends. But he got a bit too close with the camera! Can you help him to work out who is in each picture?

a.

b.

c.

d.

e.

See answers on page 93.

Memory Game

Look at this picture of Tommy and Tallulah's bedroom while you count to ten six times. Try to remember as much as you can about the picture. Then turn the page and answer the questions.

Memory Game

Questions

See answers on page 93.

Are you thinking what I'm thinking?

1. Is Tommy in the picture?

....

2. What colour are the curtains

....

3. How many books are on the floor?

....

4. What is Tallulah holding?

....

5. How many beds are in the picture?

....

6. What colour is the lamp?

....

Name Game

Tallulah is sending party invitations to her friends. Use your pencil to help her write the names on the envelopes.

 To

Madame Au Lait

 To

Chikidee

 To

Hopparoo

 To

Tommy

To

McCoggins

You're Invited

Tallulah

Paper Pals

Making these paper dolls is Easypeasy Lemon Squeezy!

Actual size templates that you can copy

Equipment

A piece of thick A4 drawing paper
A grown-up to help you
Scissors

Crayons or colouring pens
Glue
Ribbons
Fabric scraps

Always ask a grown-up to help you when using scissors.

3. Ask your grown-up to cut out the doll.

Don't cut the sides where the hands are touching.

1. Fold the drawing paper like a fan to make four columns.

2. Copy the template onto the folded paper.

Make sure that the hands touch both sides of the paper.

4. Draw the faces and colour in the clothes with crayons or colouring pens. You could draw Tommy and Tallulah, or you could create some brand-new friends to live in Tickety Town!

5. Complete your dolls by sticking ribbons and fabric scraps to decorate their clothes.

Easypeasy... Lemon Squeezy!

Song Time

There's a very special shop
With a very special clock,
And here's Tommy and Tallulah
With their very special job.
No matter what they're doing
They must always find the time
To be back inside and ready
Or the clock will never chime.
But where they're done,
It's time for fun!

Tickety Toc!
Where's your favourite place to be?
Tickety Toc!
There's things to do and friends to see.
We're watching the clock
As time goes by so quickly.
Tickety Toc!
It's easypeasy!
I spy with my little eye
something beginning with T
Tick Toc Tickety Toc Tick . . .
Tickety Toc!

Making Time

Quickerty Tickerty – it's time to make your own clock!

Tickety Toc™

12 1 2 3 4 5 6 7 8 9 10 11

Cut Out

Cut Out

Equipment

**Thick card
Paper fastener
Colouring pens
Scissors
Glue**

A grown-up to help you

Ask a grown-up to help you use the scissors.

1. Carefully cut out the three templates of the clock and the hands.

2. Decorate the clock using your favourite colours.

3. Glue the templates onto a piece of card.

4. Carefully cut around the templates.

5. Push the paper fastener through the hands and then through the centre of the clock.

6. Open the fastener at the back of the clock to hold the hands in place.

Easypeasy

Tick Toc Cheesy!

It's the splattiest time of all! It's Painting Time!

Madame Au Lait has been painting. "The Mooooona Lisa!"

"Tick Tock Tastic!" says Tommy.

"That's so good!" says Tallulah.

"Everyone's painting today!" says Madame Au Lait. "And the best painting will win this."

"The Golden Paintbrush!"

"I shall be choosing the winner before Chime Time," says Madame Au Lait.

"Our painting will be really, really good, Madame Au Lait!" says Tommy.

Tommy and Tallulah set up their easel near McCoggins's workshop.
"What shall we paint?" asks Tallulah.
"Something big." says Tommy.

"I know!" says Tallulah.
She fetches her teddy bear.

"Let's get splatting!"

Tommy and Tallulah paint the teddy bear.
"We're bound to win the golden paintbrush with this," says Tallulah.

McCoggins is setting up his easel.

"Hello, you two!" says McCoggins. "Nice day for a bit of painting!"

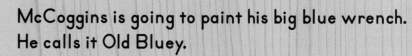

McCoggins is going to paint his big blue wrench. He calls it Old Bluey.

"I'm going to catch Old Bluey's inner beauty!" he says.

Tommy and Tallulah are worried.

"His painting's bigger than ours," Tommy whispers.

"We need something much bigger," says Tallulah. "Come on, Tommy, let's go and win the Golden Paintbrush!"

"We'll paint the Scooteroo!"

Suddenly Tommy and Tallulah hear a squawk from overhead. Chikidee is doing some painting too. Everyone wants to win the Golden Paintbrush!

Chikidee has a weather warning.

"Windy spells are expected, so beware of those extra strong gusts!"

"Thanks for the warning, Chikidee!" says Tallulah. "We're going to paint the Scooteroo!"

"I'm going to paint that enormous cloud!" says Chikidee.

Tommy and Tallulah look at each other. The cloud is bigger than the Scooteroo.

"We'll find something bigger than that cloud!" says Tallulah.

Battersby is in his shop, painting upside down. His painting is the right way up though!

DING! Tommy and Tallulah ring the bell. Battersby drops from his perch in surprise.

'Hello, Battersby,' says Tallulah.

"We need a very big canvas please," says Tommy.

"He means amazingly massive, please," Tallulah adds.

"I have the very thing," says Battersby.

Tommy and Tallulah carry their canvas to the town fountain.

"This is going to be such a big painting!" says Tommy.

"And bigger is best!" says Tallulah.

Lopsiloo is painting a giant poster of Pufferty.

Hopparoo is painting a massive mountain of carrots.

Time is running out for the painting competition.

"It will be Chime Time soon, and we haven't even started painting!" says Tommy.

"We need to paint something HUGE!" says Tallulah.

Tommy looks left and right. What does she mean?

"THE CLOCKHOUSE!" says Tallulah.

Tommy and Tallulah need a scaffold to paint their picture! They use paint rollers and hoses to spread the paint.

Well done, Tommy and Tallulah!

"It's the biggest painting ever!" says Tallulah.

Everyone arrives to look at the paintings. But just then the wind gets stronger. It makes the edge of the painting flap!

"Didn't I say it would get breezy?" Chikidee calls out.

McCoggins grabs the corner of the canvas, but the wind rips it out of the frame. It flies into the air!

Tommy and Tallulah try too, but can't hold on either.

The wind blows the painting over the front of the Clockhouse.

The painted tunnel has covered the real tunnel!

The painted track has covered the real track!

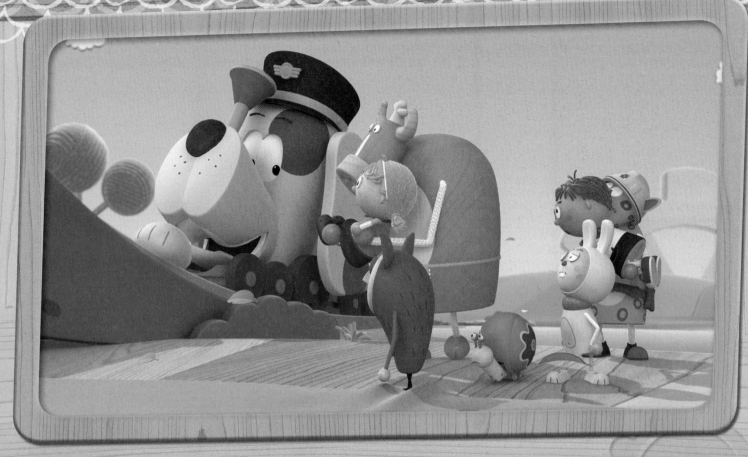

Pufferty arrives to take Tommy and Tallulah to Chime Time.
"Woof Woof! Is it Time to Chime?" he asks.

"Our painting's covering the tracks!" groans Tommy.

"We can't get to Chime Time!" says Tallulah.

"There's only one thing for it," says McCoggins. "You'll have to go through the painting!"

"Can you
break through,
Pufferty?"
asks Tallulah.

Pufferty gulps.
"I'll try-sy-try,"
he says.

Tommy and
Tallulah climb
on board, and
Pufferty steams
towards the
painting.

Faster and faster!

Closer and closer!

RIP!

Pufferty charges straight through the painting.

Yes! They did it!

Tommy and Tallulah Chime in the Time.
Then they hurry back to Tickety Town.

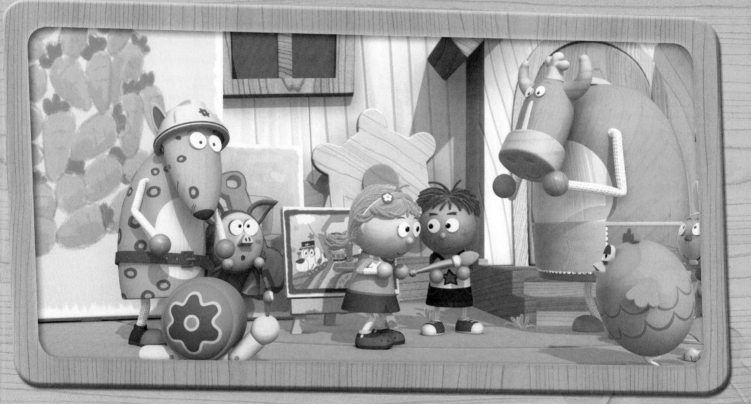

Tommy and Tallulah paint a wonderful picture of their adventure.
Madame Au Lait presents them with the Golden Paintbrush.

Tommy and Tallulah have won!

Favourites

What are your favourites? Draw some of them in these special boxes.

Everyone has favourites!

What's your favourite animal?

Tommy's favourite colour is blue.

Madame Au Lait's favourite food is cake.

What's your favourite food?

What's your favourite drink?

What's your favourite book?

What's your favourite sport?

Colouring In

McCoggins is whizzing through Tickety Town on his scooter.

Use your colouring pens to finish the picture.

McCoggins

Tickety Town is such a fun place to live! Use the number code to colour in this amazing town.

1 Purple
2 Orange
3 Red
4 Yellow
5 Pink
6 Black
7 Light Blue
8 Dark Blue
9 Light Green
10 Dark Green
11 Light Brown
12 Dark Brown

Spot the Difference

MoOOOOOOOoo!

Madame Au Lait is cooking up a yummy feast. But there are five differences between these two kitchen scenes.

Can you spot them all?

See answers on page 93.

Dot to Dot

What a tickety pickle! Who has made all this mess?
Join the dots to find out.

Match the Pairs

Match each of these friends with an object that is special for them.

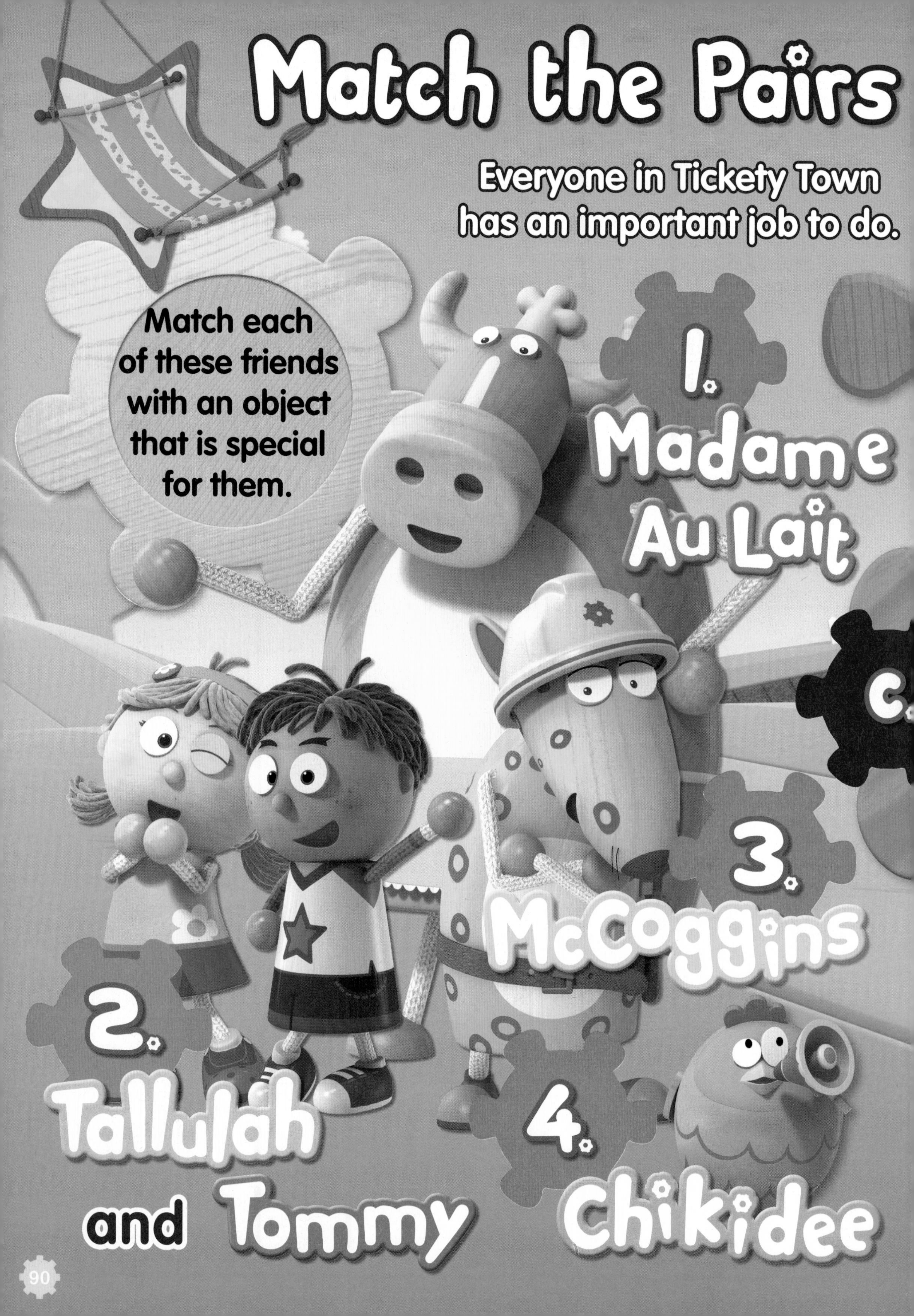

1. Madame Au Lait

2. Tallulah and Tommy

3. McCoggins

4. Chikidee

C.

90

a.

b.

d.

e.

5. Lopsiloo

91

Harvest Time

Lopsiloo has been harvesting her vegetables, and she needs your help to sort them out.

How many of each kind has she grown?

Vegetables		Number
	Carrots	
	Chillies	
	Spring Onions	
	Sweetcorn	
	Aubergines	

Answers

Page 6-7

Tommy's drum is on page 66.
Tallulah's bell is on page 67.
Madame Au Lait's Ping-Pong bat
  is on page 34.
McCoggins's spanner is on page 37.
Pufferty's ball is on page 17.
Hopparoo's hammock is on page 90.
Chikidee's knitting is on page 32.
Battersby's coat hanger is on page 41.
Lopsiloo's trowel is on page 92.
Tooteroo's binoculars are on page 30.
The Spring Chicks's tomato plant
  is on page 13.

Page 14

Page 15

1. c, 2. e, 3. a, 4. b, 5. d.

Page 16-17

Tommy, Tallulah, Battersby,
McCoggins, Hopparoo and Chikidee,
are on the train.

Page 28

Page 29

C	L	O	C	K	W	E	R
T	Y	U	A	I	O	P	A
S	D	F	K	G	H	J	K
K	L	Z	E	X	C	V	C
B	N	N	M	Q	W	W	H
W	A	V	F	U	N	B	I
B	R	Q	D	B	A	N	M
I	K	G	S	T	I	M	E

Pages 30-31

Hopparoo is eating carrots.
The Spring Chicks are eating peas.
Tooteroo is eating a red pepper.
Tommy is eating a tomato.
Tallulah is eating sweetcorn.

Page 32

Chikidee is talking to Tooteroo.

Page 36

Breakfast time: Sunny.
Dinner time: Cloudy.
Tea time: Rainy.
Bed time: Snowy.

Page 38-39

Page 41

There are 9 balls in Battersy's shop.

Page 59

Hot is the opposite of cold.
Big is the opposite of small.
Up is the opposite of down.
Empty is the opposite of full.

Page 62

1. b, 2. d, 3. c, 4. e, 5. a.

Page 63

a. Battersby.
b. Chikidee.
c. Madame Au Lait.
d. Pufferty.
e. Spring Chick.

Page 66

1. Yes.
2. Blue and white.
3. One.
4. Doll.
5. Two.
6. Purple.

Page 88

Page 89

The Spring Chicks have made
the mess.

Pages 90-91

1. d, 2. c, 3. a, 4. e, 5. b.

Page 92

8 carrots.
6 chillies.
5 spring onions.
3 sweetcorn.
2 aubergines.